Phonicability

COLLETTE DRIFTE

YEAR 1

well

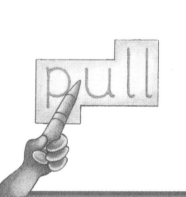

pull

g r a | | |
r | | |
a | | |

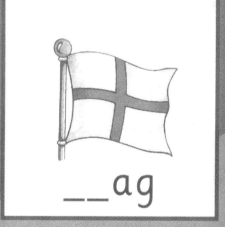

___ag

n
t → ai → l
m

b___

tap
tape

CONTENTS

Published by Hopscotch Educational Publishing Ltd,
29 Waterloo Place, Leamington Spa CV32 5LA

© 2000 Hopscotch Educational Publishing

Written by Collette Drifte
Series design by Blade Communications
Illustrated by Susan Hutchison
Cover illustration by Susan Hutchison
Printed & bound in Great Britain by
Athenaeum Press Ltd., Gateshead

ISBN 1-902239-50-4

Collette Drifte hereby asserts her moral right to be identified as the
author of this work in accordance with the Copyright, Designs and
Patents Act, 1988.

Introduction

ABOUT THE SERIES

'Throughout Key Stage 1, phonics should be the main focus of the 15-minute word level slot in the Literacy Hour.' This is the directive to be found in *Phonics, Progression in phonics: materials for whole-class teaching*, issued by the DfEE in 1999.

Phonicability is a series of books which provides individual worksheets that support and consolidate the teaching of phonics skills as outlined in the *National Literacy Strategy Framework for Teaching*. There is one book for each year of Key Stage 1(Scottish Primary 1–3): *Reception* (Scottish Primary 1), *Year 1* (Scottish Primary 2) and *Year 2* (Scottish Primary 3).

A unique feature of the series is the provision of differentiated photocopiable activity sheets aimed at considerably reducing teacher preparation time. These sheets present the same activity at three different levels – for below average ability, average ability and above average ability children. They are also differentiated across the year of work, thereby reflecting the expected progress of the child. The worksheets tie in closely with the term-by-term teaching of phonics as detailed in the *National Literacy Framework*. While they leave the teacher free to approach phonics lessons in the most appropriate way for each particular class, they provide a useful extra source of practice material to reinforce and consolidate the teaching points. It is vital that an adult reads the sheets with the children first before expecting them to start work.

Children as young as those at Key Stage 1, who are learning formal literacy and phonics rules for the first time, need a great deal of repetition, practice and consolidation. The provision of as much varied material as possible is essential. Teachers can never have too many ideas and materials for this purpose!

The contents of the books for Reception (Primary 1) and Year 2 (Primary 3) follow a similar format; this is useful for classes with mixed ages.

At the back of each book is a Record/Assessment Sheet. This details the goals for each year, as outlined in the *National Literacy Framework*, and provides a useful record of what the child has achieved and what their next targets should be.

ABOUT THIS BOOK

This book is for teachers of Year 1 children (Primary 2). It aims to:

○ provide tasks and activities which revise the work done during the Reception year, as outlined in the *National Literacy Framework*

○ provide differentiated material which will support and consolidate the phonics rules taught during the Literacy Hour, as directed for Year 1 in the *National Literacy Framework*

○ provide extension activities that can be worked on independently both during the Literacy Hour and at other (unstructured) times in the day

○ provide repetition and practice of the current rule being taught, while simultaneously reinforcing other aspects of work at word level in the *National Literacy Framework*

○ enable the children to work independently, thus allowing the teacher to work with other groups or individual children simultaneously.

THE PHOTOCOPIABLE ACTIVITY SHEETS

The differentiated sheets introduce the same phonics rule and have the same task, but at three different ability levels. They also provide a variety of activities to consolidate the same teaching point. They are designed to stimulate the children's thinking and to keep up their interest level. The format is not identical on every sheet and so the child will not suffer from 'worksheet fatigue'; boredom is guaranteed to kill motivation!

The activities on each sheet introduce the phonics rule being taught, but they also introduce and use the vocabulary of the *National Literacy Framework*, such as 'vowel', 'consonant', 'digraph' and 'blend'. While these are not among the high frequency words to be taught at Year 1, nevertheless they are words that the children need to become accustomed to hearing and using appropriately. There is a bonus also in seeing them in written form.

Some of the sheets include drawing activities. These fulfil several purposes. Correct pencil grip (tripod) can be established and maintained, hand-eye coordination will be practised and spatial awareness will be developed. Drawing style and ability, sometimes a marker to difficulties the child may be experiencing, also become apparent through these activities. An observant teacher can quickly detect any problems in these areas and remedy them early on.

The order of the activity sheets is not a recommendation to teach the sounds in the same order. They have been presented in the book to follow digraph and blend order as outlined in the *National Literacy Framework* documents. It is suggested that the teacher should read *Phonics, Progression in phonics: materials for whole-class teaching* (DfEE, 1999) and follow its suggestions for teaching order and technique. It is also important to be familiar with the pronunciations in this document.

Teaching points in the lesson plans are in line with the document's recommendations. For example, the correct technical terms are adopted (such as 'phoneme' instead of 'sound', 'digraph', 'cluster' and 'blend'). Ensure a chart is displayed in the classroom, preferably with attractive illustrations, of the digraphs and blends that must be taught throughout Year 1.

THE EXTENSION ACTIVITIES

The sheets also offer extension activities. These can be done on the back of the sheet and should be done independently, thus eliminating the need for adult supervision, although help with reading the instructions will be needed. The extension activities are designed to reinforce the work done on the main sheet and provide extra practice in the rule being taught.

ASSESSMENT

The sheets themselves build up to provide a portfolio of the child's work and progress. This is a useful resource for assessment and recording, particularly if evidence is needed at a later stage of the child's development. It is suggested that the sheets are kept in a folder or binder. A busy classroom teacher can easily lose sight of how a child performed at the beginning of the year. The sheets will provide evidence of the child's development.

THE ALIEN CHARACTER

Throughout the book (and indeed the series), a space character is used to introduce each phonics rule and to assist the children with the individual activities on the worksheet. The alien in this book is Flimp, whose name comprises an initial consonant blend, a medial vowel and a final consonant blend – all phonics rules that should be taught during this year.

When a classroom session reaches the point of using the activity sheets, introduce Flimp to the children and read the instructions on each sheet with them. While some will be able to read some of the words in the instructions, it is important that they are not just handed a worksheet but that it is talked through with them first.

SECTION CONTENT

Overall aims
This outlines the aims for the section content.

Teacher's notes
This provides information and suggestions regarding the content of the section.

Intended learning
This states the specific learning goals for the activities.

Suggested activities
This offers suggestions for activities which enable the children to practise, consolidate and reinforce the phoneme being taught. The activities are there for the teacher to pick and choose from according to the class/group needs. They are suggestions only, and as such can be adapted and altered in any way to suit the specific needs of each situation. They are varied in their nature, involving both physical and intellectual abilities.

Using the differentiated activity sheets
This explains the required tasks on the differentiated sheets. It also explains which children will benefit from a specific differentiated sheet.

Generic sheets
This provides suggestions for further activities with specific generic sheets to be found at the back of the book.

Phonicability

Year 1
Term 1.
CVC.

SECTION 1

Medial Vowels

OVERALL AIMS

○ To revise the definitions of 'phoneme' and 'vowel' and to use the terms with ease and confidence.
○ To revise c-v-c words and how to recognise and sound them.
○ To revise the vowels and to sound, recognise and name them.
○ To revise the use of the vowels in an initial position.
○ To revise the use of the vowels in a medial position, in c-v-c words.

TEACHER'S NOTES

A 'phoneme' is the smallest unit of sound in a word. For example, the word 'man' has three phonemes, 'm', 'a' and 'n'. It is vital that children learn to listen to and sound the phonemes represented by the letters of the alphabet.

Vowels as individual phonemes need to be revised and consolidated. They also need to be revised and illustrated in both initial and medial positions. The children need to revise the three-letter c-v-c word, its structure and how to sound it. Their attention should be drawn to the vowel in the medial position. (It is important to be familiar with the recommended pronunciations in *Phonics, Progression in phonics: materials for whole-class teaching* [DfEE, 1999] before introducing or revising any phoneme.)

LESSON ONE

Intended learning

○ To revise the terms 'phoneme' and 'vowel' and begin to use them appropriately.
○ To listen to, name and sound the five vowels.
○ To name an object or a word that begins with a vowel.
○ To name a three-letter word (c-v-c).
○ To name the medial vowel of any given c-v-c word.

Starting point: whole class

○ Ask 'What is a phoneme?' Remind the children that this was a word they learned last year. If necessary, teach again what a phoneme is, but with particular emphasis on the vowels.
○ Write the vowels on the board and ask what phoneme each makes. Ask the children what these five letters are called as a group. If necessary, remind them of the term 'vowel'. Ask them to identify things that begin with each vowel.
○ Ask the children to name three-letter words for each vowel, with the vowel in the medial position. Write their words on the board emphasising the medial position of the vowel.

Group activities

○ Ask the children to write a group list of all the c-v-c words they can think of. Then ask them to sort their list into five groups: words where 'a' is the medial vowel, where 'e' is the medial vowel and so on for each vowel. Which vowel sound is the most common?
○ Provide a box of mixed plastic alphabet letters and ask them to sort out only the vowels in both upper and lower cases.
○ Provide the children with an enlarged copy of a page from a magazine or newspaper. Ask them to cut out all the c-v-c words they can find. Then ask them to sort these into five groups – those with 'a' as the medial vowel, then 'e', 'i', 'o' and 'u'. Challenge them to make up sentences using the words. Can they make a sentence using one word from each pile?
○ Play a game using alphabet cards. Sort the cards into two piles, one with vowels and one with consonants. Each player takes a turn to pick up one vowel card and two consonant cards. If she can make a word, she keeps the cards. If not, the cards are returned to the bottom of the piles. The winner is the person with the most cards at the end of the game. (You might like to put some cards, such as q, x and z, to one side.)
○ Provide each child with an exercise-book dedicated to phonics work. Ask them to paste a picture (from a magazine) of something beginning with each vowel on the appropriate page.

Plenary session

○ Each group should report back on what they did. Ensure that across the term, every child has an opportunity to be their group's spokesperson. Ask them again what 'vowels' are, what the phonemes made by the vowels are and how a c-v-c word is constructed.

○ Ask what a 'phoneme' is. Give several c-v-c words and ask which are the phonemes in each one.

○ Ask questions such as, "What have you learned today?", "What did you find easy today?" and "What did you find difficult today?"

LESSON TWO

Intended learning

○ To practise saying the names and sounds of the vowels.
○ To recognise c-v-c words.
○ To identify the medial vowel in a given c-v-c word.

Starting point: whole class

○ Write the vowels on the board. Ask 'What phonemes do these vowels make?' and 'What is a phoneme?'

○ Write some c-v-c words on the board, but with the medial vowels missing. Ask for volunteers to complete the words. (It is important not to force diffident children to do this. As their confidence grows, they will be eager to volunteer when they feel ready.)

○ Play a game such as 'Grandma went to market' but buying items that either begin with a vowel, or are composed of a c-v-c word.

○ Introduce the activity sheets. Show the picture of Flimp to the children. Explain that Flimp is an alien from outer space who will be introducing to them all the phonics in this book. Explain that Flimp's name is made up of some of the phonemes they will be learning, ie initial and final consonant blends, with a medial vowel.

○ Read the instructions on each sheet to the groups.

THE DIFFERENTIATED ACTIVITY SHEETS

Activity sheet a

This is for children who need practice in recognising c-v-c words and identifying the medial vowel. It gives the opportunity to do a small amount of independent writing of c-v-c words.

Activity sheet b

This is for children who have the ability to break up a c-v-c word and identify the medial vowel. They will be able to do a little more independent writing but still need some guidance.

Activity sheet c

This is for children who are able to recognise, write and break up c-v-c words with confidence. They will be able to identify the medial vowel with little difficulty. They will also be able to do some independent writing.

Plenary session

○ Choose a child from each group to explain what their group did on their sheets. Make a display of some of the sheets while the revision work is still being done.

○ Ask questions such as, "What have you learned from today's lesson?", "Was there anything you didn't understand about today's lesson?", "What were the phonemes we revised today?" and "What were the terms we revised today?"

Match the words to the pictures.

peg

mop

jug

tin

hat

◆ Write the middle phoneme.

___ ___ ___ ___

◆ Write the middle phoneme. Then write the word.

____ ____ ____

d___ p___ c___

Write this –
a tin hat

____ ____

p___ m___

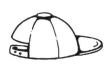

Write the middle phoneme.

10

_____   _____   _____

_____   _____

◆ Write the words.

c ____   t ____   b ____

c ____   c ____

◆ Join the words that rhyme.

dig	tin
cat	log
bun	ten
dog	wig
hen	fun
pin	hat

◆ Choose two words and write a new word that rhymes with each.

_____ _____

_____ _____

Write a sentence for one of your new words.

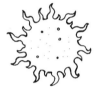

Write the words.

_____   _____   _____

_____   _____

◆Write the middle phoneme.

_____   _____   _____   _____   _____

◆Finish the words and join the ones that rhyme. Be careful!

h _ t   j _ g   c _ t

p _ g   b _ n   l _ g

t _ n   m _ g

m _ p   h _ p

◆Choose three words and write a new word that rhymes with each.

Write sentences for two of your new words.

_____ _____

_____ _____

_____

10

Phonicability

Yr 1
Term 2.
ff, ll, ss, ck, ng
bl, cr, br, tr, sk
nd, lp, st

SECTION 2

Consonant digraphs, blends and clusters

OVERALL AIMS

○ To revise the term 'digraph' and to use it appropriately and with confidence.
○ To introduce the terms 'blend' and 'cluster'.
○ To sound, recognise and name initial and final consonant digraphs, blends and clusters.
○ To name and write words that include initial and final consonant digraphs, blends & clusters.

TEACHER'S NOTES

'Digraph' is a term that the children need to learn early in their phonics sessions. It is important to revise and consolidate the term, although it will have been taught and used throughout the Reception /P1 year. This will ensure that the children use it correctly.

It is vital that children learn to listen to and sound the phonemes represented by digraphs, blends and clusters. A digraph consists of two letters giving only one phoneme (sound). For example, 'sh' or 'ff' are consonant digraphs, while 'oa' (as in 'coat') or 'ea' (as in 'seat') are vowel digraphs. A blend consists of two letters giving two phonemes. For example, 'st' as in 'stop' is an initial consonant blend; 'st' as in 'lost' is a final consonant blend. A cluster consists of three letters giving three phonemes. For example, 'str' as in 'strike' is an initial consonant cluster; 'rst' as in 'first' is a final consonant cluster.

Throughout the Reception/P1 year, the children were accustomed to learning phonemes mostly in initial positions. Now they need to focus on phonemes being in the final position in a word and be able to differentiate their sounds from the rest of the word.

LESSON ONE
Intended learning

○ To revise the term 'digraph' and to use it appropriately.
○ To focus on a phoneme in its position in a word, either initial or final.
○ To listen to, name and sound the consonant digraph, blend or cluster being taught.
○ To name a word or object that contains the consonant digraph, blend or cluster being taught.

Starting point: whole class

○ Write on the board the digraph, blend or cluster being taught and tell the children what phoneme it makes. Ask them what the correct term for two letters making a single phoneme is. If necessary, remind them that it is 'digraph' and that this is the word that they learned during their Reception Year/Primary 1. From now on, this is the term that will be used.
○ Ask several children to write the phoneme on the board, saying it out loud simultaneously. Then ask the rest of the children, "What phoneme does this digraph/blend/cluster make?"
○ Write one or two words on the board that end with the phoneme being taught. When appropriate, show the children how the phoneme is at the end of the words. Explain that it is called a 'final consonant digraph/blend/ cluster'.

○ Ask the children to give other words which include that phoneme. Give some assistance if needed. Ask for words that rhyme with any examples given.

Group activities

○ Ask the children to look through nursery rhyme or simple poetry books for words which include that digraph/blend/cluster. Write them in different-coloured felt-tipped pens on a large sheet of paper. Challenge the children to add to this list from their reading during the week.
○ Ask the children to look in a dictionary for words with the digraph/blend/cluster. Make the words with plastic letters in a tray. Keep the tray as a display while the phoneme is being taught.
○ Provide the children with an enlarged copy of a page from a magazine or newspaper. Ask them to cut out all the words they can find with the digraph/blend/cluster. They could draw a picture and write a sentence to go with it using a selection of these words. Make the drawings and sentences into a class book to share.
○ Make wordsearches where the children have to find words with the chosen digraph/blend/ cluster.
○ Use Generic sheet 1 to make word slides for the digraph being taught.

Plenary session

○ Each group should report back on what they did. Use the large sheet of paper containing nursery rhyme words to discuss the phoneme. Display it while the digraph/blend/cluster is being taught and consolidated. Do the same with the tray of plastic letters/words.

○ Ask the children questions such as, "What word have you revised today?", "What does it mean?", "What was the consonant digraph/blend/cluster you learned today?", "What did you find difficult today?" and "What did you find easy?"

LESSON TWO

Intended learning

○ To recognise, name and sound the consonant digraph/blend/cluster being taught.

○ To practise writing the letters representing the digraph/blend/cluster.

○ To practise using the digraph/blend/cluster in its appropriate position in a word.

Starting point: whole class

○ Write the previous lesson's digraph/blend/cluster on the board. Ask, "What phoneme does this digraph/blend/cluster make?", "What is a digraph/blend/cluster?" and "What words end/begin with this digraph/blend/cluster?"

○ Ask for three or four volunteers to write words on the board.

○ Introduce the activity sheets. Read the instructions on each sheet to the groups.

THE DIFFERENTIATED ACTIVITY SHEETS

Activity sheets a

These are for children who need repetition of the digraph/blend/cluster being taught. They encourage them to look carefully at the formation of the digraph/blend/cluster, both as an entity and in its position in a word.

Activity sheets b

These are for children who are able to do a little independent writing. They encourage them to look carefully at the formation of the digraph/blend/cluster and to place it in its position in a word.

Activity sheets c

These are for children who can confidently write a few words independently. They encourage them to look carefully at the formation of the digraph/blend/cluster and to place it in its position in a word.

Plenary session

○ Choose a child from each group to explain what their group did on their sheets. Ensure that across the term, every child has an opportunity to be their group's spokesperson.

○ Make a display of some of the sheets while that digraph/blend/cluster is still being taught and consolidated.

○ Ask questions such as, "What have you learned from today's lesson?", "Was there anything you didn't understand about today's lesson?", "What was the digraph/blend/cluster we learned today?" and "What phoneme does it make?"

○ Ask the children to think of some words where the digraph/blend/cluster comes in the middle.

GENERIC SHEETS

○ Use Generic sheet 1 to make word slides for the appropriate consonant digraph/blend/cluster.

○ Use Generic sheet 2 to make Bingo cards when enough consonant digraphs/blends/clusters have been taught.

14

Colour red the squares with *ff*.

Flimp

ff	*tt*	*bb*	*ff*
dd	*ff*	*pp*	*tt*
bb	*ff*	*dd*	*ff*

◆How many did you find?

I found ☐ squares with *ff*.

◆Draw a circle around all the *ff* words you can see.

wobble   sniff   riddle

bubble   little

puff   bottle   stiff

◆How many did you find?

I found ☐ *ff* words.

Write this –
puff

Colour blue the squares with *ff*.

Flimp

tt	ff	bb	ff
ff	bb	ff	dd
ll	ff	pp	ff
ff	dd	ff	tt

◆ How many did you find? Finish the sentence.

I found _____

◆ Draw a circle around all the *ff* words you can see.

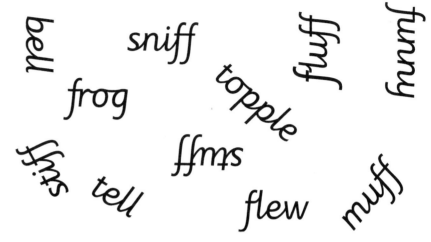

bell sniff fluff funny frog topple ffuts tell flew muff

◆ How many did you find? Finish the sentence.

I _____

Write one of the words you found.

Colour green the squares with *ff*.

Flimp

ff	*tt*	*ff*	*dd*	*ff*
u	*ff*	*ff*	*ff*	*pp*
ff	*ff*	*bb*	*tt*	*ff*
ff	*u*	*ff*	*ff*	*dd*

◆ How many did you find? Finish the sentence.

I _____

◆ Draw a circle around all the *ff* words you can see.

muff pill fluff bell huff

stuff stiff bluff crafty sell letter flat

stiff

◆ How many did you find? Finish the sentence.

I _____

◆ Look in a dictionary for the words you don't know.

Write the words you found.

16

Look at these shapes with *u* words in them.

◆Write the same words in these shapes.

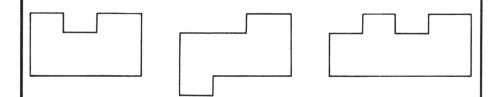

◆Draw a picture of one of the words.

◆Join the words to the pictures.

  well

shell

doll

bell

  ball

◆Write *u* to make more words.

mi _____

bu _____

gu _____

Write a sentence for one of the *u* words.

18

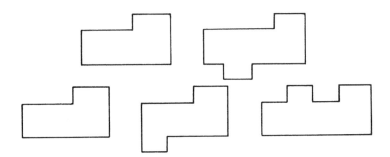

Look at these shapes with *u* words in them.

Flimp

| well | spell |
| ball | pull | shell |

◆Write the same words in these shapes.

◆Draw pictures of two of the words.

◆Write the words under the pictures.

ba _____   _____   _____

_____   _____

◆Write a sentence for two of the words.

_____

_____

Write two more *u* words.

Look at these shapes with *u* words in them.

spell   smell   ball

bell   shell   fall   well

◆ Write the same words in these shapes.

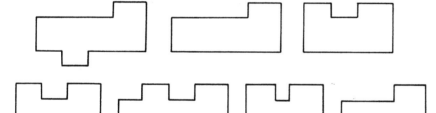

◆ Draw pictures of three of the words.

◆ Write a sentence under each picture.

 **bell**

_____

ball

_____

 **well**

Write three more *u* words.

_____

20

Write *ss* to finish the words.

gla__ dre__ me__

◆ Draw pictures of two of the words. Write the words under the pictures.

_____ _____

◆ Finish the crossword by writing *ss*.

g	r	a		
l				
a				

◆ Write the words.

_____

_____

Write a sentence for one of the words.

Write *ss* to finish the words.

gra__ me__

dre__ ki__ gla__

◆Draw pictures of two of the words. Write the words under the pictures.

_____   _____

◆Finish the crossword by writing **ss**.

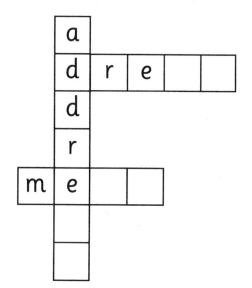

◆Write the words.

Write sentences for two of the words.

_____

_____

_____

22

Finish these *SS* words.

cla__ dre__ ki__
addre__ gla__ le__

◆Draw pictures for three of the words.

◆Write a sentence for one of the words.

_____

◆Finish the *SS* crossword.

◆Write the words.

Write sentences for three of the words.

_____

_____

_____

_____

Write in the beginning phonemes of these *ck* words.

du

 sock

_____ *ck*   _____ *ck*

 duck

clo

_____ *ck*

so

◆Write the words.

_____   _____   _____

◆Draw a duck with a long neck.

◆Write the sentence.

A duck _____

_____

Draw a black sack.
Write this –
a black sack

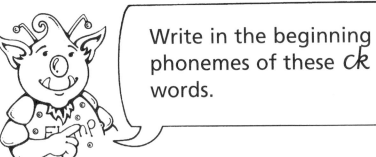

Write in the beginning phonemes of these *ck* words.

sa

bri

sti

ro

so

_____ ck

_____ ck

_____ ck

_____ ck

_____ ck

◆ Write the words.

_____   _____

_____

◆ Draw a duck in a sack.

◆ Write the sentence.

A duck _____

_____

◆ Make more *ck* words.

clo _____

bla _____

li _____

Write a sentence for one of these *ck* words.

Write the *ck* words.

_____   _____

sock   *duck*

stick   *sack*

_____

clock   *brick*

_____

◆ Draw a brick on a truck.

◆ Write the sentence.

_____

◆ Make more *ck* words.

ne _ _

ki _ _

bla _ _

ba _ _

si _ _

Write sentences for two of these words.

PHONICABILITY **YEAR 1**

25

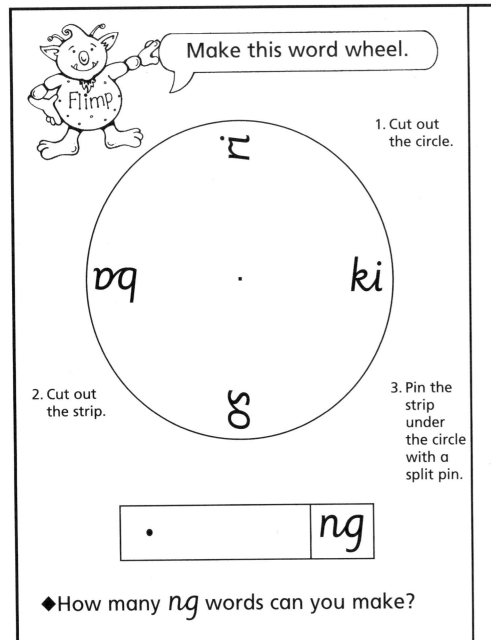

Make this word wheel.

1. Cut out the circle.

2. Cut out the strip.

3. Pin the strip under the circle with a split pin.

◆How many *ng* words can you make?

◆Write the *ng* words from your word wheel here.

_____   _____

_____   _____

◆Draw pictures of two of the *ng* words.

Write a sentence for one *ng* word.

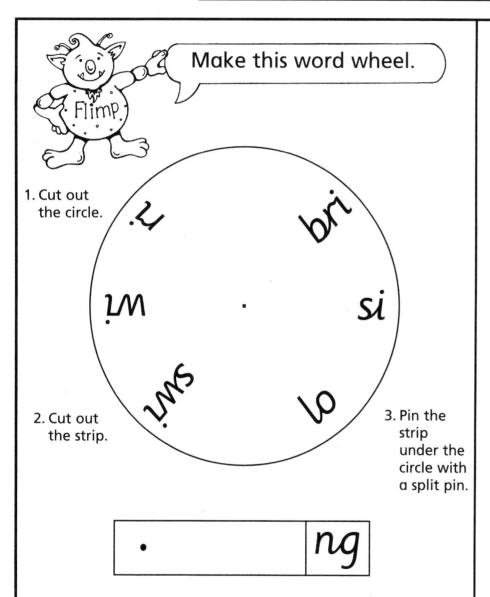

Make this word wheel.

1. Cut out the circle.

2. Cut out the strip.

3. Pin the strip under the circle with a split pin.

◆How many *ng* words can you make?

◆Write the *ng* words from your word wheel here.

_____   _____

_____   _____

_____   _____

◆Draw pictures of two of the *ng* words.

Write sentences for two of the *ng* words.

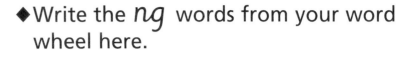

Make this word wheel.

1. Cut out the circle.

2. Cut out the strip.

3. Pin the strip under the circle with a split pin.

ng

◆How many **ng** words can you make?

◆Write the **ng** words from your word wheel here.

_____   _____   _____

_____   _____   _____

_____   _____

◆Draw pictures of two of the **ng** words.

Write sentences for three of the **ng** words.

Draw a line from each picture to **bl** or **br**.

bl

br

◆ Write **bl** or **br** to make a word.

_ _ ue   _ _ own

_ _ ick   _ _ ack

◆ Draw a brown brick and a blue brush.

Write this –
a brown brick and
a blue brush

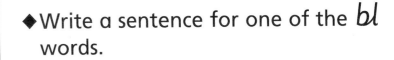

Write **bl** or **br** to finish each word.

__ __ indfold

__ __ ush

__ __ ead

__ __ ood

◆ Write a sentence for one of the **bl** words.

_____

◆ Write a sentence for one of the **br** words.

_____

◆ Draw a black brick.

Write two more **bl** words and two more **br** words.

Write a *bl* word or a *br* word under each picture.

_____

_____

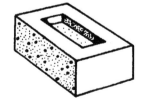

_____

◆Write sentences for the words.

_____

_____

_____

_____

◆Draw a blue bridge.

Write one more *bl* word and one more *br* word. Write a sentence for each word.

Flimp

Draw a clown.

◆Write the word. _____

Draw a crown.

Flimp

◆Write the word. _____

◆Find the words in the grid and colour them in. One has been done for you.

clap

crab

c̶l̶o̶w̶n̶

clock

crown

club

cross

c	l	o	c	k	c
c	r	c	r	a	b
e	c	r	o	s	s
d	c	l	o	w	n
f	g	c	l	u	b
c	c	l	a	p	c
a	c	r	o	w	n

◆Write a new *cl* word and a new *cr* word.

Write a sentence for one of your new words.

_____

_____

Flim

Draw a cloud.

◆ Write the word. _____

Draw a crane.

◆ Write the word. _____

◆ Find the words in the grid and colour them in. One has been done for you. You may go across or down.

cliff
cream
~~cloud~~
clock
crown
clip
crab
clown
crib

c	c	l	i	f	f
r	c	c	c	l	r
e	l	c	l	i	p
a	o	r	o	c	l
m	u	i	c	r	r
c	d	b	k	o	l
c	c	l	o	w	n
c	r	a	b	n	r

◆ Look in a dictionary for any words that you don't know.

Write sentences for two of the words.

34

Draw some clothes.

Flimp

◆Write the word. _____

Draw a crocodile.

Flimp

◆Write the word. _____

◆Find the words in the grid and colour them in. One has been done for you. You may go across or down.

crane
clip
cross
clown
cracker
crab
class
cry
claw
crown
clap

c	l	w	p	c	l	a	p
c	l	i	p	r	c	p	c
r	c	r	m	o	r	c	l
a	c	l	f	s	c	l	c
c	l	a	s	s	l	o	r
k	c	r	e	l	a	w	a
e	r	c	r	o	w	n	n
r	y	c	r	a	b	y	e

◆Look in a dictionary for any words that you don't know.

Write sentences for three of the words.

Flim

Write the final phonemes in the circles to make *dr* words.

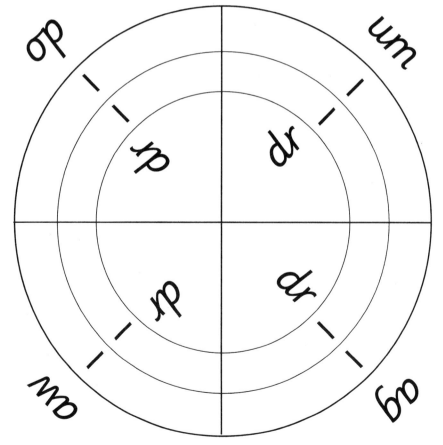

◆ Write the *dr* words.

_____

_____

_____

_____

◆ Now see if you can find some *dw* words in a dictionary.

Write a new *dr* word.
Write a *dw* word.

Write the final phonemes in the circle to make *dr* words.

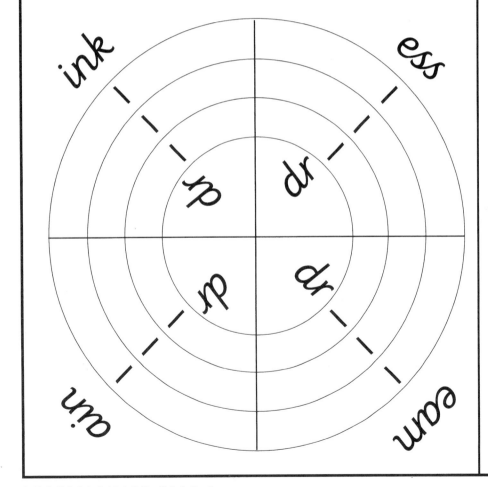

ink

ess

dr

dr

dr

dr

ain

eam

◆ Write the *dr* words.

_____

_____

_____

_____

◆ Write one *dr* word in a sentence.

_____

◆ Now see if you can find some *dw* words in a dictionary.

Write two new *dr* words.
Write a *dw* word.

Write the final phonemes in the circles to make *dr* words.

Flimp

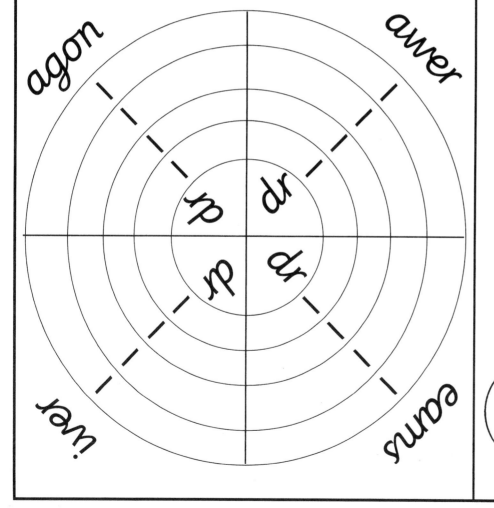

agon

awer

dr   dr

dr   dr

iver

sums

◆ Write the *dr* words.

_____

_____

_____

_____

◆ Write sentences for two of the *dr* words.

_____

_____

◆ Now see if you can find some *dw* words in a dictionary.

Write three new *dr* words.
Write a *dw* word.

38

 Write *fl* or *fr* to finish the words.

 __ og

__ ag

__ uit

__ ower

◆ Write the words in the *fl* box or the *fr* box.

fl

fr

 Write a new word in each box.
Draw pictures of your words.

Write *fl* or *fr* to finish the words.

__ __ uit

__ __ ame

__ __ y

__ __ og

__ __ own

__ __ ower

◆ Write the words in the *fl* box or the *fr* box.

fl

fr

Write two new words in each box. Draw pictures of your words.

Write the *fl* or *fr* words. You may look in a dictionary if you like.

_____

_____

_____

_____

◆ Write three new words in each box.

fl

fr

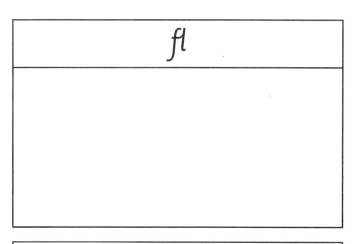

Write sentences for two of your new words. Draw pictures of them.

Colour blue the things that begin with *gl*.
Colour green the things that begin with *gr*.

◆ Write *gl* or *gr* to finish the words.

_ _ ass   _ _ ove

_ _ apes   _ _ ass

◆ Write a new *gl* word.

_____

◆ Write a new *gr* word.

_____

Write sentences for your new words.

42

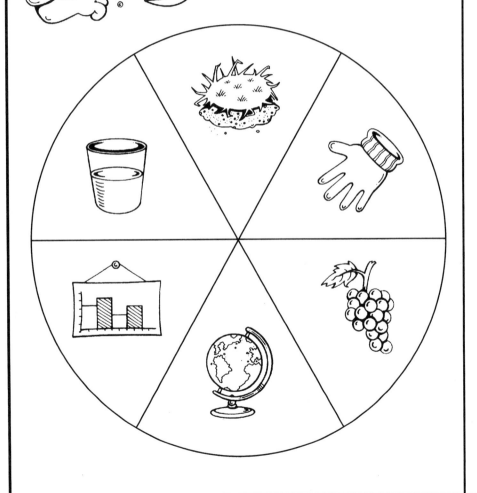

Colour red the things that begin with *gl*.
Colour yellow the things that begin with *gr*.

◆ Write *gl* or *gr* to finish the words.

_ _ *apes*   _ _ *ass*

_ _ *ove*   _ _ *aph*

_ _ *ass*   _ _ *obe*

◆ Write a new *gl* word.

_____

◆ Write a new *gr* word.

_____

Write sentences for your new words.
Find some more in a dictionary.

Colour yellow the things that begin with *gl.*
Colour blue the things that begin with *gr.*

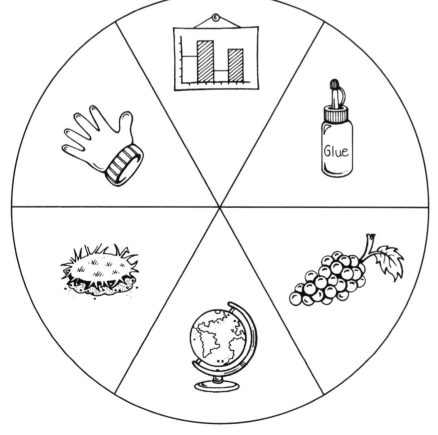

◆Write the *gl* and *gr* words. You may look in a dictionary if you like.

_____   _____

_____   _____

_____   _____

◆Write a sentence for two of the words.

_____

_____

Write two new *gl* words and two new *gr* words.
Write sentences for them.

44

Put a red circle around all the *pl* words.
Put a blue circle around all the *pr* words.

plum

black

pan

plan

pram

present

pot

brown

◆ Draw a pram. Write the word.

pr _____

◆ Draw a plum. Write the word.

pl _____

Find one new *pl* and one new *pr* word. Write a sentence for each of them.

Put a green circle around all the *pl* words.
Put a blue circle around all the *pr* words.

plate   price   pegs

plum

pots   black

pram   phone

pans   pretty

plane   brown

◆ Write a sentence for one of the *pl* words.

_____

◆ Write a sentence for one of the *pr* words.

_____

◆ Draw a plum in a pram.

Find two new *pl* and two new *pr* words. Write them in sentences.

45

46

Put a red circle around all the *pl* words.
Put a yellow circle around all the *pr* words.

plum   pots   print

pretty   brown   plate

photo   pans

black   pram   please

plant   phone   price

◆Write sentences for two *pl* words and two *pr* words.

_____

_____

_____

_____

_____

◆Draw a pretty plant pot on a pretty plate.

How many new *pl* and *pr* words can you find?
Write them.

Write **SC** or **sk** to finish the words.

__ __ _arf_

__ __ _irt_

__ __ _rew_

__ __ _ip_

◆ Write **SC** or **sk** to finish the crossword.

	i	r	t
	p	
a		
r	e	w
f		

◆ Write the words here.

_____   _____

_____   _____

Draw pictures of the words.

48

Write **SC** or **sk** to finish the words.

Flimp

__ __ales

__ __ittles

__ __arf

__ __irt

__ __ate

__ __rew

◆ Write **SC** or **sk** to finish the crossword.

```
        |i|
        |r|
 |i|t|t|l|e|s|
|a|
|t|           |a|r|f|
|r|e|w|        |l|
                |e|
                |s|
```

◆ Write the words here.

_____   _____

_____   _____

Draw a picture of each word.

Write **SC** or **sk** to finish the words.

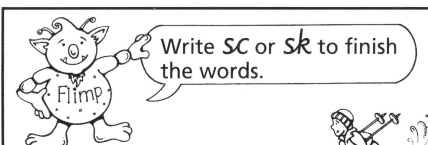

__ __ales

__ __i

__ __irt

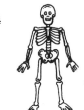
__ __rew

__ __arf

__ __eleton

__ __ar

__ __ull

◆Write **SC** or **sk** to finish the crossword.

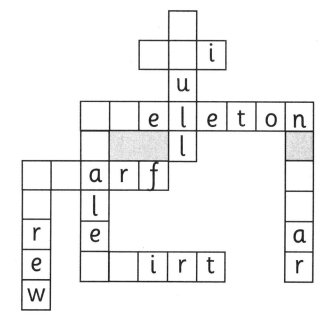

◆Write the words here.

_____   _____   _____

_____   _____   _____

_____   _____

Draw a picture of each word.

Look at these shapes with *sl* or *sm* words in them.

◆Write the words in the empty shapes.

 slow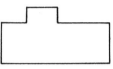

 smoke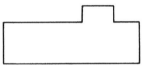

 slug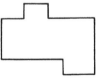

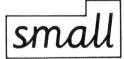 small

◆Write the words here.

_____   _____

_____   _____

◆Write *sl* or *sm* to finish the words.

__ide   __ile

◆Draw a picture of one of the words.

Find a new *sl* word and a new *sm* word. Write them.

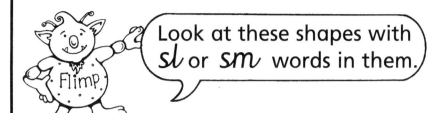

Look at these shapes with **sl** or **sm** words in them.

slug slow smell

smoke sleep smooth

◆Write the words in the empty shapes.

◆Write **sl** or **sm** to finish the words.

__ice   __ooth

__ell   __ip

__ide   __ile

◆Draw a picture of one of the words.

Find two new **sl** words and two new **sm** words. Write them.

Look at these shapes with *sl* or *sm* words in them.

slate   smooth   sledge

smack   sleep   smelly

sleeve   smart

◆Write the words in the empty shapes.

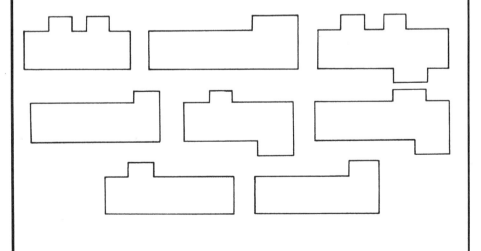

◆Write a sentence for one *sl* word and one *sm* word.

_____

_____

◆Draw a picture of one of the words.

Find two more *sl* words and two more *sm* words. Write them.

52

Flimp

1. Cut out the box and carefully cut along the lines.

2. Cut out these strips and slide them through the slits.

sn	sp

sn	sp
ow	in
ap	oon
iff	ade
ail	ell

3. What words can you make?
   Read them aloud.

Write your *sn* and *sp* words.

54

Flimp

1. Cut out the box and
   carefully cut along
   the lines.

2. Cut out these strips and slide them
   through the slits.

sn   sp

sn

ail

ap

iff

ow

ore

sp

ear

oon

ark

end

it

3. What words can you make?
   Read them aloud.

Write your *sn* and
sp words.

Flimp

1. Cut out the box and carefully cut along the lines.

2. Cut out these strips and slide them through the slits.

sn	sp
ake	ider
eeze	y
ore	eak
atch	ell
ail	ace
iff	oon

sn   sp

3. What words can you make? Read them aloud.

Write your *sn* and *sp* words.

Draw a star.

◆ Write the word. _____

Draw a sweet.

◆ Write the word. _____

◆ Find the *st* and *sw* words in the grid and colour them in. One has been done for you.

f	s	s	w	a	n
s	t	a	r	b	w
s	s	t	a	m	p
w	s	t	e	p	m
t	s	s	w	i	m
s	w	i	n	g	w
g	s	t	i	c	k

star
swim
stick
swan
step
~~stamp~~
swing

◆ Write a new *st* word and a new *sw* word.

Write a sentence for one of your new words.

_____

_____

Draw a stamp.

Flimp

◆Write the word. _____

Draw a swan.

Flimp

◆Write the word. _____

◆Find the *st* and *sw* words in the grid and colour them in. One has been done for you. You may go across or down.

stand

sweet

~~stamp~~

steam

swing

stick

swim

stone

sweep

s	w	s	w	i	m
t	s	t	a	m	p
s	w	e	e	p	k
s	e	a	s	t	w
t	e	m	s	w	i
s	t	i	c	k	n
s	t	o	n	e	g
t	s	t	a	n	d

◆Look in a dictionary for any words that you don't know.

Write sentences for two of the words.

58

Draw a stick.

◆Write the word. _____

Draw a swan swimming.

◆Write the words. _____

◆Find the *st* and *sw* words in the grid and colour them in. One has been done for you. You may go across or down.

swim
star
stamp
swan
station
switch
~~stick~~
steam
swap
stand
swing

s	t	a	m	p	u	t	w
w	s	t	e	a	m	w	t
i	w	s	s	s	w	i	m
t	s	t	a	t	i	o	n
c	w	i	s	a	s	t	s
h	a	c	s	n	w	w	t
t	n	k	t	d	a	w	a
s	w	i	n	g	p	s	r

◆Look in a dictionary for any words that you don't know.

Write sentences for three of the words.

Colour red the squares with *scr*.
Colour yellow the squares with *squ*.

scr	qua	spr	squ
squ	str	scr	qui
squ	spr	que	scr

◆How many did you find?

I found [ ] squares with *scr*.

I found [ ] squares with *squ*.

◆Draw a blue circle around each *scr* word and a green circle around each *squ* word.

scrap   strong   squash

squeeze   spring   scrub

quiz   storm   string   question

◆How many words did you find?

I found _____ *scr* words.

I found _____ *squ* words.

Write the words you found.

Colour blue the squares with *scr*.
Colour green the squares with *squ*.

scr	que	spr	squ
squ	str	scr	que
spr	scr	squ	str
que	squ	qui	scr

◆How many did you find?

I found ☐ squares with *scr*.

I found ☐ squares with *squ*.

◆Draw a red circle around each *scr* word and a yellow circle around each *squ* word.

screw   spring   question   squeak

quiz   scrape   squash   scrub

square   special   quarrel

◆How many words did you find?

Write the words you found.

I found _____ *scr* words.

I found _____

Colour green the squares with *scr*.
Colour yellow the squares with *squ*.

que	squ	spr	scr	qui
scr	str	squ	que	scr
squ	spr	scr	qui	str
str	scr	que	squ	squ

◆ How many did you find?

I found ☐ squares with *scr*.

I found _____

◆ Draw a blue circle around each *scr* word and a red circle around each *squ* word.

queen   strong   squash

squirrel   scratch

question   scream   screw

scrub   square   quiz   squirt

spring   string

◆ How many words did you find?

I found _____

_____

Write the words you found.

62

Look at the picture.

Flimp

◆Join **spl** to the right ending.

| spl |

| ing |

| ash |

◆Write the word. _____

◆Look at the picture.

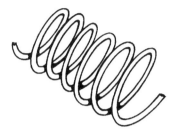

◆Join **spr** to the right ending.

| spr |

| ing |

| ash |

◆Write the word.

_____

Can you find more **spl** and more **spr** words?

Look at the pictures. Join **spl** to the right endings.

spl   ing   it

◆ Write the word. _____

spl   ash   ay

◆ Write the word. _____

◆ Look at the pictures. Join *spr* to the right endings.

spr   ash   ay

◆ Write the word. _____

spr   it   ing

◆ Write the word. _____

Can you find more *spl* and more *spr* words?

Look at the pictures. Write the correct endings on the *spl* words.

it   inter   ash

spl _____

ash   it   inter

spl _____

inter   ash   it

spl _____

◆Look at the pictures. Write the correct endings on the *spr* words.

ing   ead   ay

spr _____

ash   ay   it

spr _____

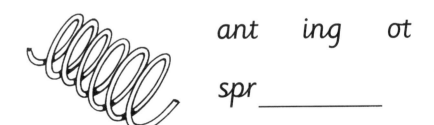

ant   ing   ot

spr _____

Can you find more *spl* and more *spr* words?

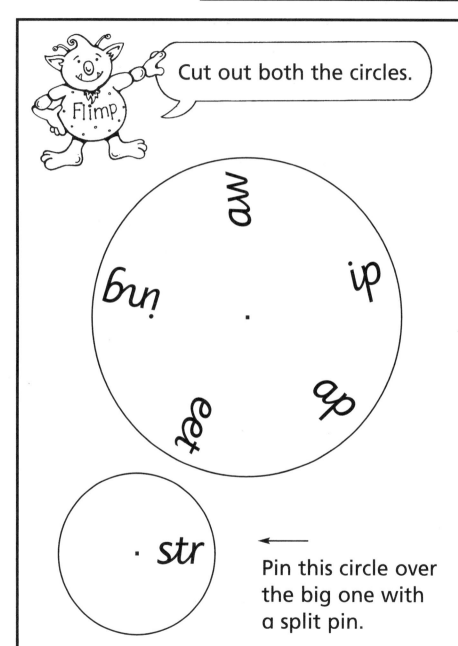

Cut out both the circles.

Pin this circle over the big one with a split pin.

◆Write the *str* words you can make with your *str* wheel.

str _____

_____

_____

_____

_____

Write a sentence for two of your *str* words.

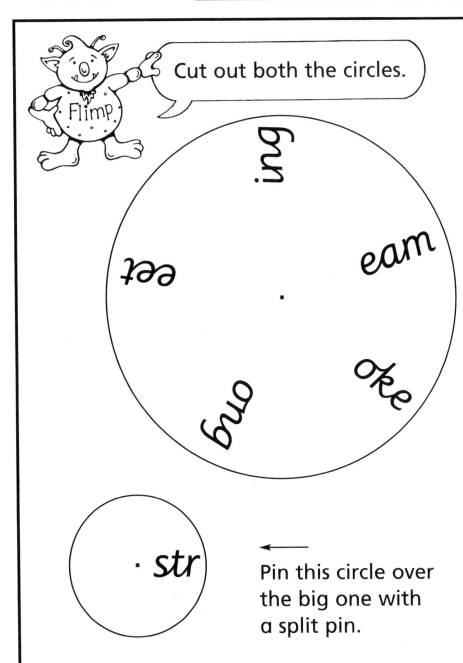

Cut out both the circles.

ing

eam

eet

ong

oke

· str

← Pin this circle over the big one with a split pin.

◆ Write the *str* words you can make with your *str* wheel.

_____

_____

_____

_____

_____

_____

Write sentences for two of your *str* words.
Find some more *str* words.

66

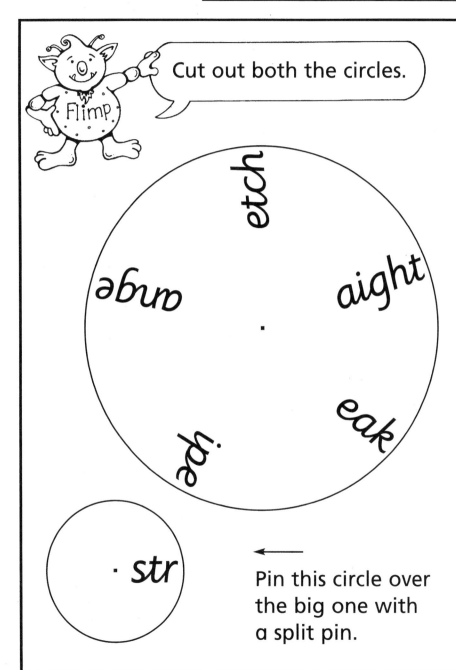

Cut out both the circles.

Pin this circle over the big one with a split pin.

◆ Write the *str* words you can make with your *str* wheel.

_____

_____

_____

_____

_____

Write a sentence for three of your *str* words. Find some more *str* words.

Put a green circle around the *tr* words and a yellow circle around the *tw* words.

tree

three

twig

top

twins

train

triangle

twelve

tap

tin

toes

◆ Write the *tr* and *tw* words that you drew circles around.

tr _____

_____

_____

tw _____

_____

_____

◆ Choose one word and draw a picture.

Find one new *tr* word and one new *tw* word. Write sentences for them.

Put a red circle around the *tr* words and a blue circle around the *tw* words.

thing   tear   twist

truck

trim   test

twelve

twice   three   tools   tray

tramp   top   twig

◆ Write the *tr* and *tw* words that you drew circles around.

tr   **tw**

_____   _____

_____   _____

_____   _____

_____   _____

◆ Choose one word and draw a picture.

Find two new *tr* words and two new *tw* words. Write them in sentences.

70

Put a blue circle around the *tr* words and a green circle around the *tw* words.

tractor twelve

twinkle

top

three

tin

twins

triangle

treasure

twenty

thirty

ten

true twice traffic

◆Write the *tr* and *tw* words that you drew circles around.

_____   _____

_____   _____

_____   _____

_____   _____

◆Choose one word and draw a picture.

Find three new *tr* and three new *tw* words. Write them in sentences.

Write *shr* or *thr* to finish the words.

Flimp

_____ one

_____ imp

◆Look in a dictionary to find out what they mean.

◆Look in a dictionary for two new *shr* words and two new and *thr* words. Write them in the boxes.

shr
1.
2.

thr
1.
2.

Write your words in sentences.

Flim

72

Write *shr* or *thr* to finish the words.

Flimp

_____ed

_____ead

_____oat

_____ug

◆ Look in a dictionary to find out what they mean.

◆ Look in a dictionary for three new *shr words* and three new *thr* words. Write them in the boxes.

shr
1.
2.
3.

thr
1.
2.
3.

Write your words in sentences.

Write *shr* or *thr* to finish the words.

_____ ush

_____ ink

_____ eat

_____ oat

_____ iek

_____ ug

◆Look in a dictionary to find out what they mean.

◆Find four new *shr* words and four new *thr* words in a dictionary. Write them in the boxes.

shr
1.
2.
3.
4.

thr
1.
2.
3.
4.

Write your words in sentences.

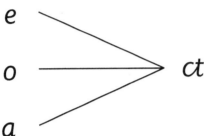

Which letter will go with *ct* to make a word?

e

o ———> *ct*

a

◆ Write the word. _____

◆ Which letters will go with *ft* to make a word?

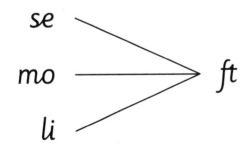

se

mo ———> *ft*

li

◆ Write the word. _____

◆ Draw a circle around every *ct* and a square around every *ft*.

tt   ff   ct   ft

ct

ft   at   ft   at   tt

at   tt

ct   at   ff   ct

tt   ft

◆ How many did you find? ☐ *ct*   ☐ *ft*

Can you find some more *ct* and *ft* words? Use a dictionary to help you.

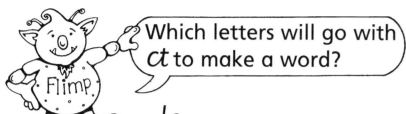

Which letters will go with *ct* to make a word?

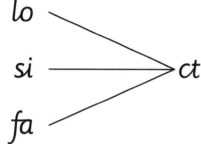

lo
si ——————> ct
fa

◆ Write the word. _____

◆ Which letters will go with *ft* to make a word?

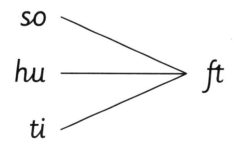

so
hu ——————> ft
ti

◆ Write the word. _____

◆ Draw a triangle around every *ct* and a circle around every *ft*.

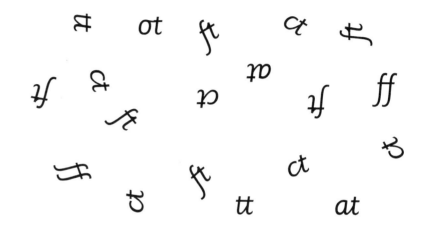

◆ How many did you find? ☐ *ct*   ☐ *ft*

Can you find more *ct* words and more *ft* words? Use a dictionary to help you.

76

Which letters will go with *ct* to make a word?

spri

shri ————➤ ct

stri

◆Write the word.   _____

◆Which letters will go with *ft* to make a word?

cho

thu ————➤ ft

shi

◆Write the word.   _____

◆Draw a square around every *ct* and a triangle around every *ft*.

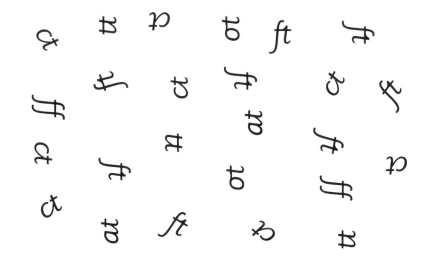

◆How many did you find?   ☐ *ct*   ☐ *ft*

Can you find more *ct* words and more *ft* words? Use a dictionary to help you.

Cross out the wrong *ld* words.

Flimp

sold old gold

old cold gold

◆Write the correct words.

_____

_____

◆Cross out the wrong *nd* words.

hand sand land

bond pond land

◆Write the correct words.

_____

_____

Write one of the words in a sentence.

Cross out the wrong *ld* words.

sold gold cold

cold gold old

hold cold gold

◆Write the correct words.

_____ _____ _____

◆Cross out the wrong *nd* words.

band land sand

send mend lend

mend lend send

◆Write the correct words.

_____

_____

_____

Write some of the words in sentences.

Cross out the wrong *ld* words.

◆Cross out the wrong *nd* words.

sand

mend

send

send

mend

bend

old gold hold

sold cold told

sand

land

pond

cold hold old

mild wild cold

lend

pond

wand

◆Write the correct words.

◆Write the correct words.

Write some of the words in sentences.

_____   _____   _____   _____

_____   _____   _____   _____

These words are mixed up. Can you sort them out? Here is a clue: the final phonemes are *lk* or *nk*.

◆ Find the same words in the grid and colour them in. You may go across or down.

kusl ⟶ [ ]

bkna ⟶ [ ]

snik ⟶ [ ]

klim ⟶ [ ]

sink
milk
bank
sulk

c	j	f	s	b	b
g	e	h	u	d	a
p	m	i	l	k	n
s	i	n	k	z	k

◆ Choose one word and draw a picture.

Write a sentence for one *lk* word and one *nk* word.

These words are mixed up. Can you sort them out? Here is a clue: the final phonemes are *lk* or *nk*.

lkis   ⟶   ☐

nkiw   ⟶   ☐

skul   ⟶   ☐

knat   ⟶   ☐

mkli   ⟶   ☐

knip   ⟶   ☐

◆ Find the same words in the grid and colour them in. You may go across or down.

e	w	m	i	l	k
s	i	l	k	p	d
u	n	f	q	i	g
l	k	j	r	n	o
k	t	a	n	k	h

silk
wink
sulk
tank
milk
pink

◆ Choose one word and draw a picture.

Write sentences for two of the words.

Can you sort out these mixed-up words? The final phonemes are *lk* or *nk*.

klmi ————→ ▭

lsku ————→ ▭

njuk ————→ ▭

ksin ————→ ▭

wkni ————→ ▭

slki ————→ ▭

tkna ————→ ▭

◆ Find the same words in the grid and colour them in. You may go across or down.

a	s	i	n	k	c
c	u	l	k	j	e
t	l	f	s	u	g
a	k	w	i	n	k
n	m	i	l	k	p
k	h	q	k	r	d

milk
junk
sulk
wink
silk
tank
sink

◆ Choose one word and draw a picture.

Write sentences for three words.

82

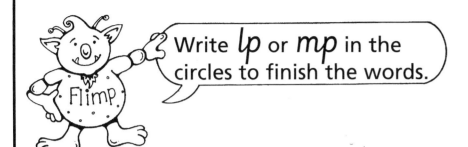

Write **lp** or **mp** in the circles to finish the words.

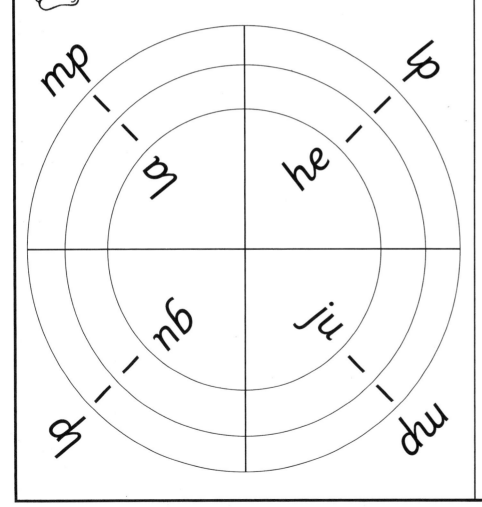

mp

lp

g

he

mb

ju

lp

mp

◆Write the words.

_____ **lp**

_____ **mp**

_____

_____

◆Look for the words in a dictionary.

Write a new **lp** word.
Write a new **mp** word.

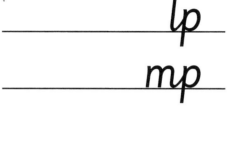

84

Write *lp* or *mp* in the circles to finish the words.

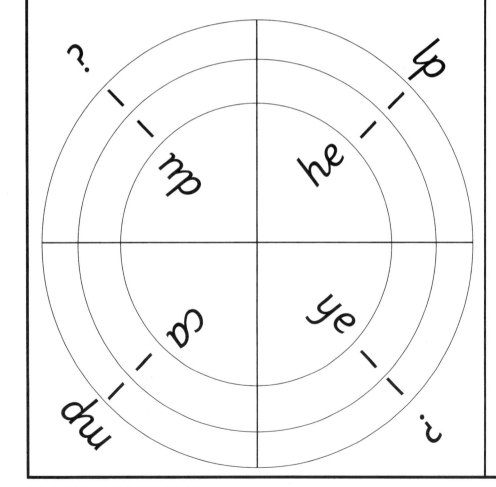

◆ Write the words.

_____

_____

_____

_____

◆ Look for the words in a dictionary.

Write two new *lp* words.
Write two new *mp* words.

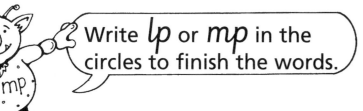

Write *lp* or *mp* in the circles to finish the words.

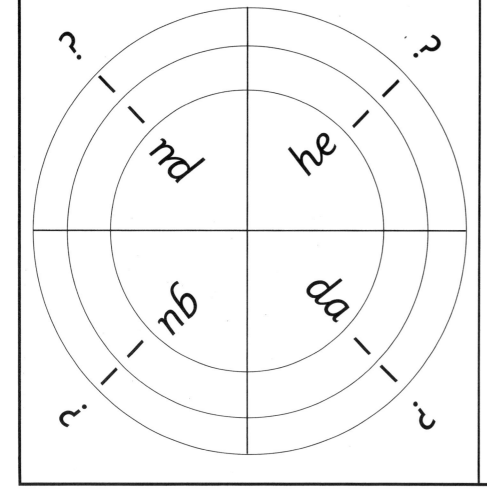

◆ Write the words.

_____

_____

_____

_____

◆ Look for the words in a dictionary.

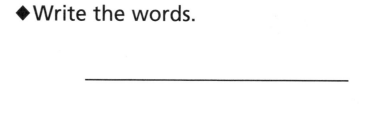

Write sentences for two of the words.
Find a new *lp* word and a new *mp* word.

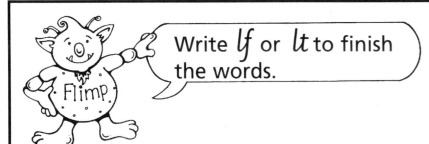

Write _lf_ or _lt_ to finish the words.

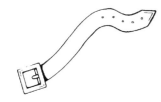

be _____

e _____

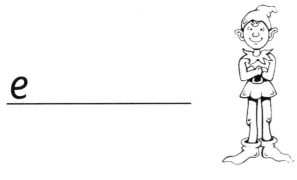

◆Do the crossword. All the answers are _lf_ or _lt_ words.

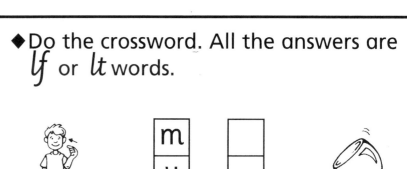

m	
y	

Look for the words in a dictionary.

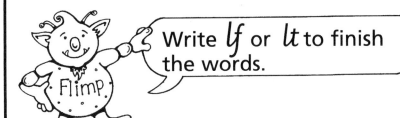

Write *lf* or *lt* to finish the words.

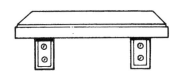

she _____

sa _____

◆ Do the crossword. All the answers are *lf* or *lt* words.

m y

Look for the words in a dictionary.

Write *lf* or *lt* to finish the words.

myse_____

ki_____

◆Do the crossword. All the answers are *lf* or *lt* words.

Look for the words in a dictionary.

Write the *lth* and *nch* words in the empty boxes.

Flimp

bench

health

◆ Write the words again.

_____

_____

◆ Draw a picture of one of the

◆ Look for the words in a dictionary.

Can you find more *lth* and *nch* words?

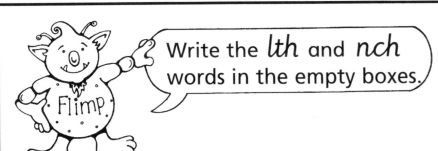

Write the *lth* and *nch* words in the empty boxes.

lunch

filth

munch

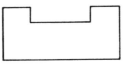

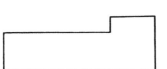

◆ Write the words again.

_____

_____

_____

◆ Draw pictures of two of the words.

◆ Look for the words in a dictionary.

Can you find more *lth* and *nch* words?

Write the *lth* and *nch* words in the empty boxes

Flimp

wealth

bench

crunch

lunch

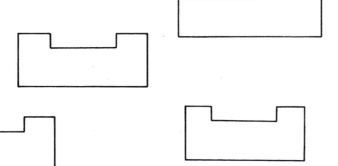

◆ Write the words again.

_____

_____

_____

_____

◆ Look for the words in a dictionary.

◆ Write a sentence for one of the words.

_____

Can you find more *lth* and *nch* words?

Flimp

Which phonemes go with _nt_ to make words?

Flimp

go

te   pa

hu

fe   ja

◆Write the words.

_____

_____

_____

◆Next, draw a pink ant.

◆Next, write _This is a pink ant._

_____

◆Next, write a word that ends in _xt._

_____

Write your _xt_ word in a sentence.

Which phonemes will go with *nt* to make words?

ju   ta   se   wa   we   be   lo   fi   pa

◆Write the words.

_____ _____ _____

_____ _____

◆Next, draw a bent pin.

◆Next, write *Here is a bent pin.*

_____

◆Next, write a word that ends in *xt.*

_____

Write your *xt* word in a sentence.

Which phonemes will go with *nt* to make sensible words?

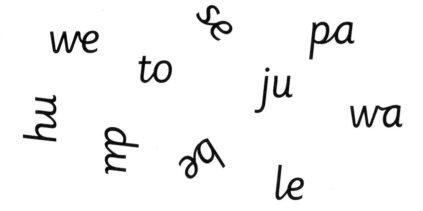

◆ Write the words.

_____ _____ _____

_____ _____ _____

_____

◆ Next, draw a green and pink tent.

◆ Next, write a sentence for your picture.

_____

◆ Next, write a word that ends in *xt*. _____

Write your *xt* word in a sentence.

Flimp

1. Cut out the box and carefully cut along the lines.

2. Cut out these strips and slide them through the slits.

95

st   pt

st
lo
du
fa
ju

pt
we
sle
cre
swe

3. What words can you make?
   Read them aloud.

Write the words you made.

Flimp

1. Cut out the box and carefully cut along the lines.

2. Cut out these strips and slide them through the slits.

st   pt

pt
cre
sle
ado
swe
we

st
be
fi
pe
li
fa

3. What words can you make? Read them aloud.

Write the words you made.

Flimp

1. Cut out the box and carefully cut along the lines.

2. Cut out these strips and slide them through the slits.

pt	st
ado	po
sle	te
we	fa
swe	mi
ada	ru
cre	be

st   pt

3. What words can you make? Read them aloud.

Write the words you made.

98

Colour red the squares with *sk*. Colour yellow the squares with *sp*.

sl	sk	st	sp
sk	sl	sp	sh
sp	sh	sl	sk

◆ How many did you find?

I found ☐ squares with *sk*.

I found ☐ squares with *sp*.

◆ Draw a circle around each *sk* word and each *sp* word.

wasp   fast   west   mist

wash   desk   mask   just

fish   crisp   best

◆ How many words did you find?

I found _____ *sk* words.

Write the words you found.

I found _____

Colour blue the squares with *sk*. Colour green the squares with *sp*.

sk	st	sh	sp
sp	sl	sk	sh
sh	sk	sp	st
sl	sp	sh	sk

◆How many did you find?

I found ☐ squares with *sk*.

I found ☐ _____

◆Draw a circle around each *sk* word and each *sp* word.

mask

wish

crisp

fast

pest

tusk

wasp

fish

best

lisp

desk

just

◆How many words did you find?

I found _____ *sk* words.

Write the words you found.

I found _____

100

Colour green the squares with **sk**. Colour blue the squares with **sp**.

sp	sh	sk	st	sp
sk	sl	sp	sk	sh
st	sp	sl	sh	sk
st	sk	sh	sl	sp

◆How many did you find?

I found ▢ squares with **sk**.

I _____

◆Draw a circle around each **sk** word and each **sp** word.

wasp   fish   desk   fish

task   rasp   clasp   lisp   flask   crisp

whisk   mask

last   last   just   best

◆How many words did you find?

_____

_____

Write the words you found.

◆Look in a dictionary for the words you don't know.

Phonicability

Yr 1
Term 3.

SECTION 3

Long vowels

Long vowels

OVERALL AIMS

○ To sound, recognise and name vowel digraphs with long vowel phonemes.
○ To name and write words that include the long vowel phonemes.
○ To be aware how the addition of a final 'e' alters a short vowel to a long one.
○ To be able to name and write words that are altered by the addition of a final 'e'.

TEACHER'S NOTES

A digraph consists of two letters giving only one phoneme (sound). For example, 'sh' or 'ff' are consonant digraphs, while 'oa' (as in 'coat') or 'ea' (as in 'seat') are vowel digraphs. The long vowels taught in this chapter are vowel digraphs which have a long vowel phoneme (as opposed to a short vowel phoneme). For example, 'oa' as in 'coat' as opposed to 'o' as in 'cot'; the same phoneme is achieved by adding a final 'e', such as 'rob' becoming 'robe'.

It is vital that children learn to listen to and sound the phonemes represented by digraphs, and vowel digraphs are no exception to this. The children must have the ability to hear a word in its different components if they are to develop sound reading and spelling skills. Thus they need to be able to recognise the formation of vowel digraphs and the resulting phonemes, in order to sound a word successfully. Similarly, they need to know the effect of the addition of a final 'e' on a short vowel.

LESSON ONE

Intended learning

○ To introduce the term 'vowel digraph' and to use it appropriately.
○ To learn the common long vowel digraphs, as outlined in the *National Literacy Framework*.
○ To listen to, name and sound the long vowel digraph being taught.
○ To name a word or object that contains the long vowel digraph being taught.

Starting point: whole class

○ Write the digraph being taught on the board and tell the children what phoneme it makes. Tell the children that this is a vowel digraph which gives a long vowel phoneme.
○ Play a game-in-the-round where the children take it in turns to say a word with that phoneme. The words may or may not rhyme – saying the correct phoneme is the important part. For example, 'bread' and 'leaf' are correct – they have the same phoneme but don't rhyme.
○ Share the page of a magazine and draw a ring around each word containing the vowel digraph. Ask for volunteers to write the discovered words on the board.

Group activities

○ Ask the children to make a word tree of the vowel digraph being taught. The trunk is labelled with the digraph and the leaves all have a word written on them which contains that digraph.
○ Ask the children to make a collection of objects/pictures/models of things with the digraph in the names. Keep these on display while the digraph is being taught.
○ Make word wheels to contain words illustrating the digraph being taught.
○ Use Generic sheet 1 to make word slides for the digraph being taught.
○ Use Generic sheet 2 to play Bingo when enough vowel digraphs have been learned.

Plenary session

○ Each group should report back on what they did. Use the digraph tree to discuss the phoneme. Display it while the digraph is being taught and consolidated. Do the same with the collection of objects/models/pictures.
○ Ask the children, "What was the vowel digraph you learned today?", "What is the short vowel phoneme?" and "What is the long vowel phoneme when it has become a vowel digraph?"

LESSON TWO

Intended learning

○ To recognise, name and sound the vowel digraph being taught.
○ To practise writing the letters representing the digraph.
○ To practise using the digraph in words and sentences.
○ To learn the effect on a short vowel of the addition of a final 'e'.

Starting point: whole class

○ Write the previous lesson's digraph on the board. Ask the children what phoneme this vowel digraph makes. Ask them to tell you what other words have this digraph in them. Then ask them what happens to a short vowel when you add 'e' at the end of a word.
○ Ask for three or four volunteers to write some words on the board that demonstrate this.
○ Introduce the activity sheets. Read the instructions on each sheet to the groups.

THE DIFFERENTIATED ACTIVITY SHEETS

Activity sheets a

These are for children who need repetition of the vowel digraph. They encourage them to look carefully at the formation of the digraph. They help to develop the ability to differentiate between similar words to identify the one which is required, and to discover others with the same phoneme. They give practice in looking at, sounding and writing the long vowel being taught.

Activity sheets b

These are for children who are able to do a little independent writing and who are capable of doing more work on a sheet. They encourage them to look carefully at the formation of the digraph. They give practice in looking at, sounding and writing of long vowel being taught. They encourage the writing of simple sentences incorporating the digraph being taught.

Activity sheets c

These are for children who can confidently write a few words independently. They encourage them to look carefully at the formation of the digraph. They give practice in looking at, sounding and writing the long vowel being taught. They encourage the writing of more sentences incorporating the digraph being taught.

Plenary session

○ Choose a child from each group to explain what their group did on their sheets. Ensure that across the term, every child has an opportunity to be their group's spokesperson.
○ Make a display of some of the sheets while that digraph is still being taught and consolidated.
○ Ask, "What have you learned from today's lesson?", "Was there anything you didn't understand?", "What was the vowel digraph we leared today?", "What phoneme does it make?" and 'What happens when you add 'e' at the end of a word?'

GENERIC SHEETS

○ Use Generic sheet 1 to make word slides for the appropriate vowel digraph.
○ Use Generic sheet 2 to make Bingo cards when enough vowel digraphs have been taught.

Draw a circle around the right *ee* or *ea* words.

 sweep sheep

tree teeth

 leaf lead

steam seat

◆ Find the same words in the grid and colour them in. You may go across or down.

s	h	e	e	p	l
e	t	s	e	d	e
a	t	e	e	s	a
t	e	e	t	h	f

leaf
sheep
seat
teeth

◆ Write a sentence for two of the words.

_____

_____

Find more *ee* and *ea* words.

Draw a circle around the right *ee* or *ea* words.

Flimp

steep sleep

meal mean

peel preen

leaf lead

peas please

sweep sleet

◆ Find the same words in the grid and colour them in. You may go across or down.

s	w	e	e	p	s
l	e	a	d	e	p
e	a	m	e	a	e
e	m	e	a	l	a
p	e	e	l	e	s

sweep
peas
lead
peel
sleep
meal

◆ Write a sentence for three of the words.

_____

_____

_____

Find more *ee* and *ea* words.

Flim

Draw a circle around the right *ee* or *ea* words.

Flimp

wheel   wheeze

beans   beat

three   tree

steam   stream

meat   mean

queen   queer

tea   tear

feet   feel

◆ Find the same words in the grid and colour them in. You may go across or down.

w	h	e	e	l	a
e	b	e	a	n	s
t	e	a	f	e	t
t	r	e	e	a	e
q	u	e	e	n	a
m	e	a	t	e	m

wheel
beans
tree
steam
meat
queen
tea
feet

◆ Write a sentence for four of the words.

_____

_____

_____

_____

Find more *ee* and *ea* words.

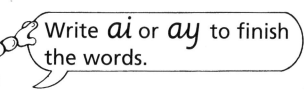

Write *ai* or *ay* to finish the words.

ch__n

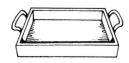

tr__

pl__

tr__n

◆Write the words.

_____   _____

_____   _____

◆Make words from the phonemes.

d
h   ay   _____
p   _____
                       _____

n
t   ai →l   _____
m   _____

Write a sentence for one *ai* word and one *ay* word.

107

Write *ai* or *ay* to finish the words.

Flimp

r__n

May

M__

h__

m__l

◆Write the words.

_____   _____

_____   _____

◆Make words from the phonemes.

ch

pl   *ai* → n

r

_____

_____

_____

s

l   *ay*

w

_____

_____

_____

Write sentences for two *ai* words and two *ay* words.

Flimp

Write the *ai* or *ay* words.

_____

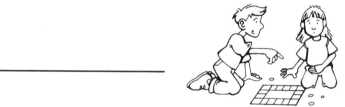

_____

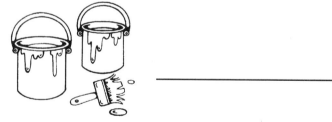

_____

_____

◆ Make words from the phonemes.

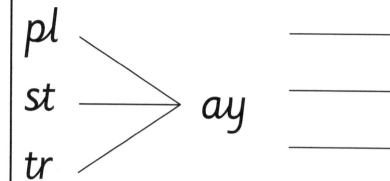

pl
st   ay
tr

_____

_____

_____

tr
ag   ai → n
br

_____

_____

_____

Write the words in sentences.

10

Cut out both the circles.

tr

pl

ight ·

ied

y

Pin this circle
over the big one
with a split pin.

◆Write down the real words you can
make with your wheel.

_____

_____

_____

_____

_____

_____

Write two of the
words in sentences.

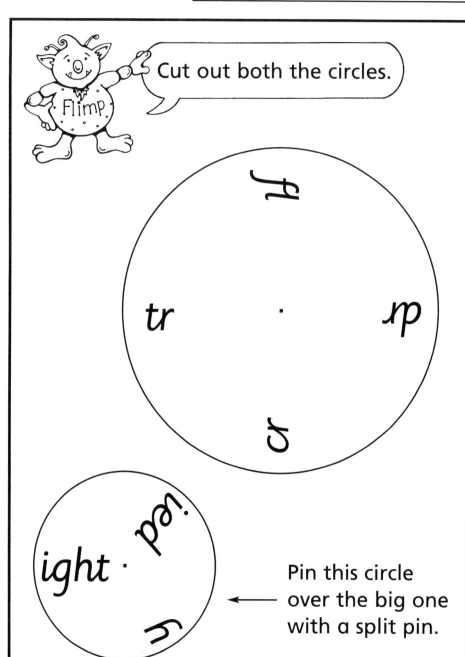

Cut out both the circles.

Flimp

fl

tr · dr

cr

ight · ied

y

Pin this circle over the big one with a split pin.

◆Write down the real words you can make with your wheel.

_____

_____

_____

_____

_____

_____

_____

_____

Write three of the words in sentences.

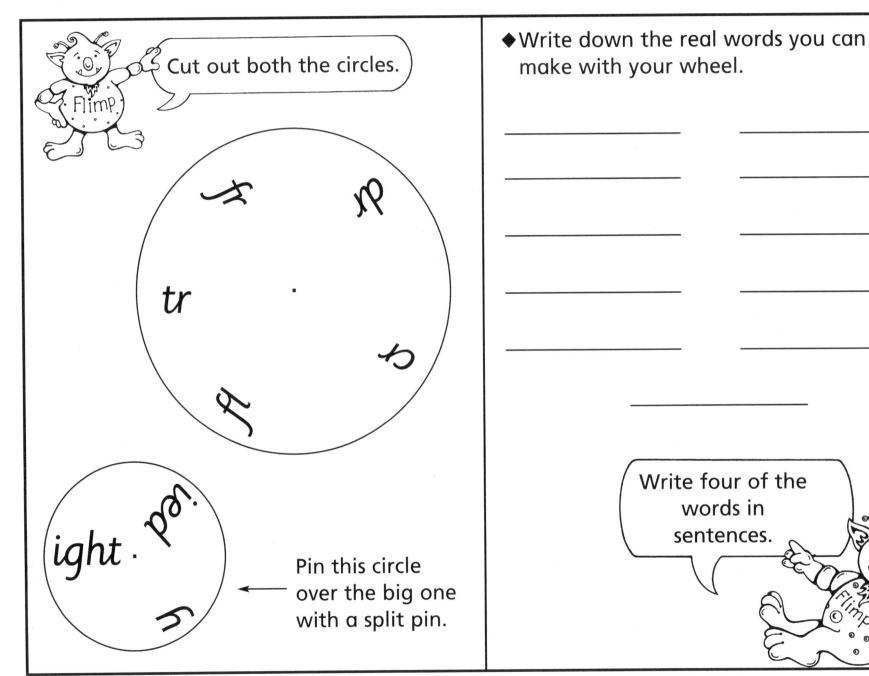

Cut out both the circles.

Pin this circle over the big one with a split pin.

◆Write down the real words you can make with your wheel.

_____   _____

_____   _____

_____   _____

_____   _____

_____   _____

_____

Write four of the words in sentences.

How many words can you make from the **oa** circle?

g   c

d   **oa**   t

r

_____   _____

◆Write **ow** to finish the words.

sn __ __

b __ __

t __ __

bl __ __

Write one **oa** word and one **ow** word in sentences.

How many words can you make from the **oa** circle?

Flimp

m f g

oa

l   d

c   r

t

_____   _____

_____   _____

◆ Write the **ow** words.

b__l

arr__

___

___ ___

Write some of the words in sentences.

How many words can you make from the **oa** circle?

Flimp

b   r   c   t   g   f   l   ch   p   s   d

oa

_____   _____

_____   _____

_____   _____

_____   _____

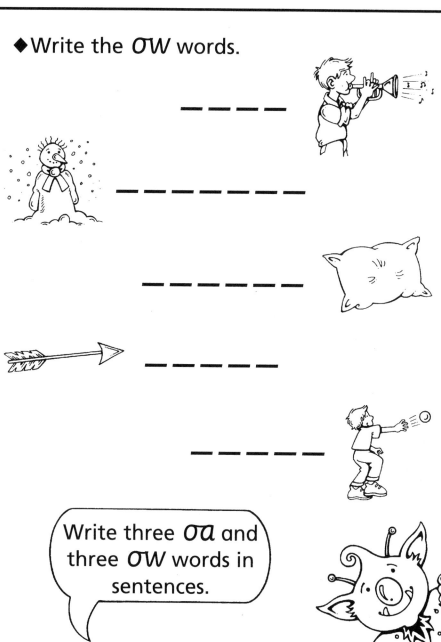

◆ Write the **ow** words.

_ _ _ _ _

_ _ _ _ _ _ _

_ _ _ _ _ _

_ _ _ _ _

_ _ _ _ _

Write three **oa** and three **ow** words in sentences.

Here is a fool on a stool.

Coo – *oo*, *ew*
and *ue* all say
'oooo'!

◆ Read these words aloud.

moon

chew

glue

◆ Put a circle around the *oo* words that are hidden in the word line.

coatmoonloafgoalboottoad

◆ Put a circle around the *ew* words.

cheatcleanchewstreetnewleaf

◆ Put a circle around the *ue* words.

elbowmoatbluegreengluelean

Find new words for
oo, *ew* and *ue*.
Write the words.

116

Here is a fool on a stool.

Coo – *oo*, *ew* and *ue* all say 'oooo'!

◆ Read these words aloud.

boot   tool

flew   stew

blue   true

◆ Put a circle around the *oo* words that are hidden in the word line.

loaftoolcoatfoalboottoadmoonleaf

◆ Put a circle around the *ew* words.

clearmeanfleweatstewteamchewlean

◆ Put a circle around the *ue* words.

moatoutblueloaftruegoatrudesoap

Find two new words for *oo*, *ew* and *ue*. Write the words.

Here is a fool on a stool.

Coo – oo, ew and ue all say 'oooo'!

◆Read these words aloud.

roof   pool   soon

chew   flew   screw

clue   rude   true

◆Put a circle around the oo words that are hidden in the word line.

coatroofloafmoanpoolfoalsoonloaf

◆Put a circle around the ew words.

meaneatchewleanflewmeatscrewnear

◆Put a circle around the ue words.

loudcluegrainrudeloafgoattruered

Find three new words for oo, ew and ue. Write the words.

119

Draw a line from each picture to the right word.

Flimp

tap
tape

pipe
pip

◆ Add **e** to change the words.

hat + e ——→ _____

pin + e ——→ _____

◆ Read the words aloud.

mat   man

bit   din

◆ Write them with **e** on the end and read them aloud again.

_____   _____

_____   _____

Write two of the words in sentences.

Flim

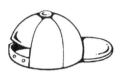

Match the words to the pictures.

cap

cape

pine

pin

◆ Add e to change the words.

bit + e ⟶ _____

mat + e ⟶ _____

◆ Read the words aloud.

can   tap   hat

pin   win   spit

◆ Write them with e on the end and read them aloud again.

_____   _____

_____   _____

_____   _____

Write two of the words in sentences.

120

Draw a line from each picture to the right word.

Flimp

kite

kit

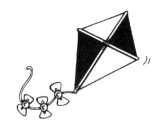

man

mane

◆Add **e** to change the words.

tap + e ——→ _____

rid + e ——→ _____

◆Read the words aloud.

fat   pan   mad   cap

fin   bit   shin   pip

◆Write them with **e** on the end and read them aloud again.

_____   _____

_____   _____

_____   _____

_____   _____

Write two of the words in sentences.

Flim

Read the words aloud.

not   rod

cub   cut

◆Write them with **e** on the end and read them aloud again.

_____   _____

_____   _____

◆Do the crossword.

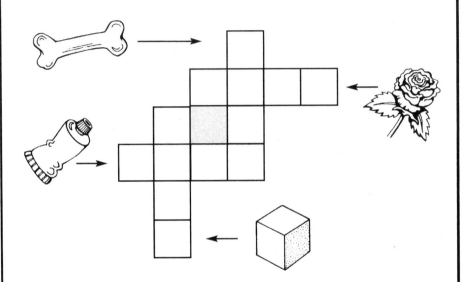

◆Write the words.

_____   _____

_____   _____

Write two of the words in sentences.

Read the words aloud.

rob   mop   not

cut   tub   cub

◆Write them with **e** on the end and read them aloud again.

_____   _____

_____   _____

_____   _____

◆Do the crossword.

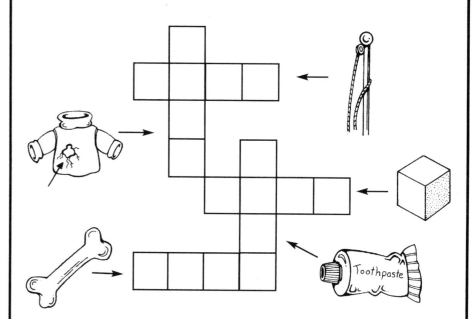

◆Write the words.

_____

_____

_____

_____   _____

Write three of the words in sentences.

123

24

Read the words aloud.

Flimp

cut us tub cub

hop rod mop not

◆Write them with e on the end and
read them aloud again.

_____ _____

_____ _____

_____ _____

_____

◆Do the crossword.

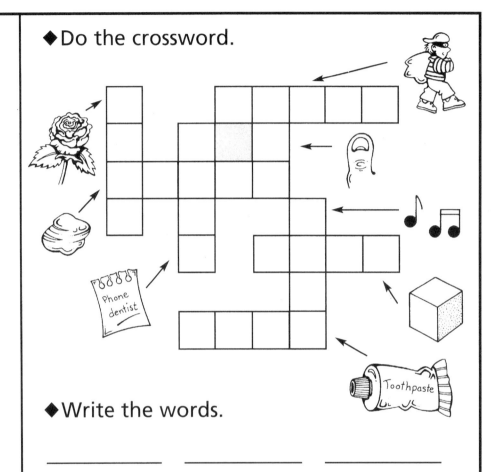

◆Write the words.

_____ _____ _____

_____ _____ _____

_____

Write four
of the words
in sentences.

Phonicability

SECTION 4

Generic Sheets

Use this sheet to
make word slides
for the phoneme
being taught.

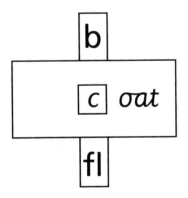

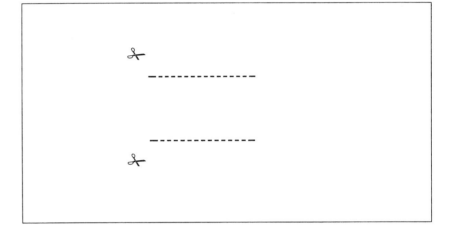

Generic Sheet 2

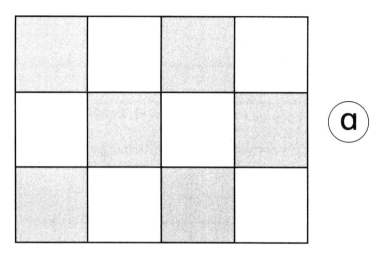

a

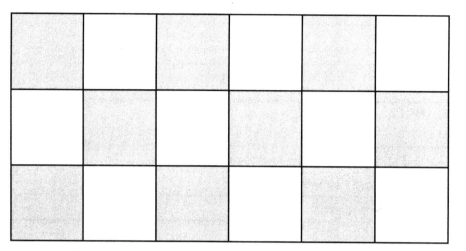

b

c

These grids can be used to make phoneme Bingo cards. Grid ⓐ is for the children who complete ⓐ sheets; grid ⓑ is for the children who complete ⓑ sheets; grid ⓒ is for the children who complete ⓒ sheets.

Phonics Record/Assessment Sheet

Name

Year   Level   Date

TARGET SKILL		NLSF REFERENCE
(Step 4)		
1 Can hear and say phonemes in the medial position a/e/i/o/u		YR
2 Can segment and spell c-v-c words		2b, 2c 2e, 4c
3 Can blend to read c-v-c words		Y1 Term 1: 4, 5, 6
(Step 5)		Y1
1 Can segment and spell c-c-v-c words and c-v-c-c words		Term 2: 3
2 Can blend to read c-c-v-c words and c-v-c-c words		
(Step 6)		Y2 Term 1: 1, 2, 3
1 Knows the ten vowel phonemes: digraphs ai, ee, ie, oa, oo, or, ar, ir, oi, ou		
2 Can segment to spell words containing vowel phonemes represented by more than one letter		Y1
3 Can blend to read words containing vowel phonemes represented by more than one letter		Term 3: 1

Relevant Comments: